car
et or

v.mar

0161

THE PERFECTLY WONKY CARROT

Written and illustrated
by Newmany

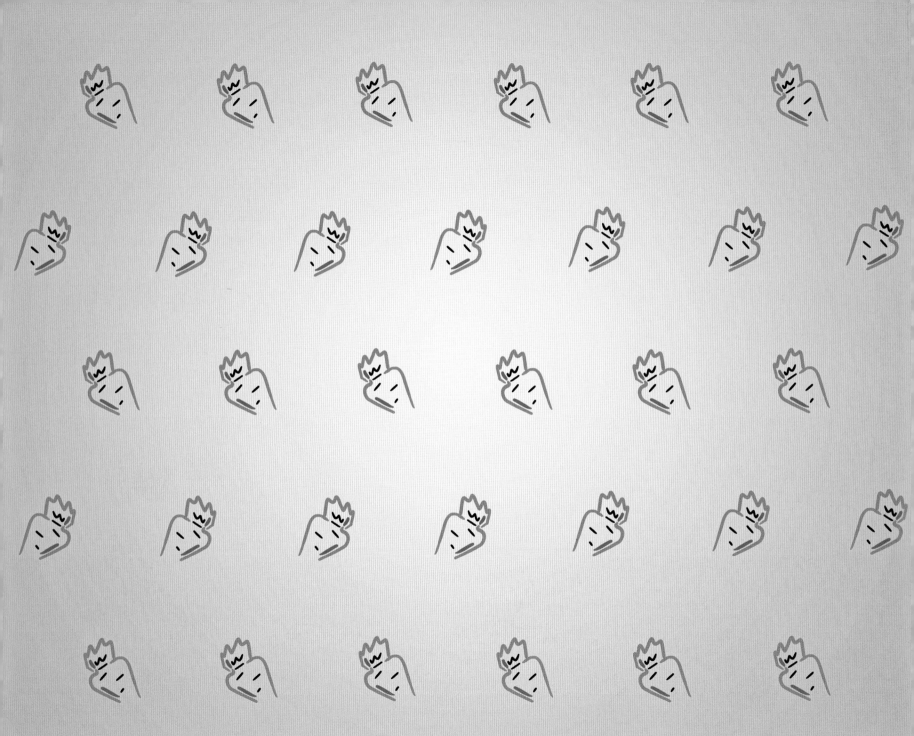

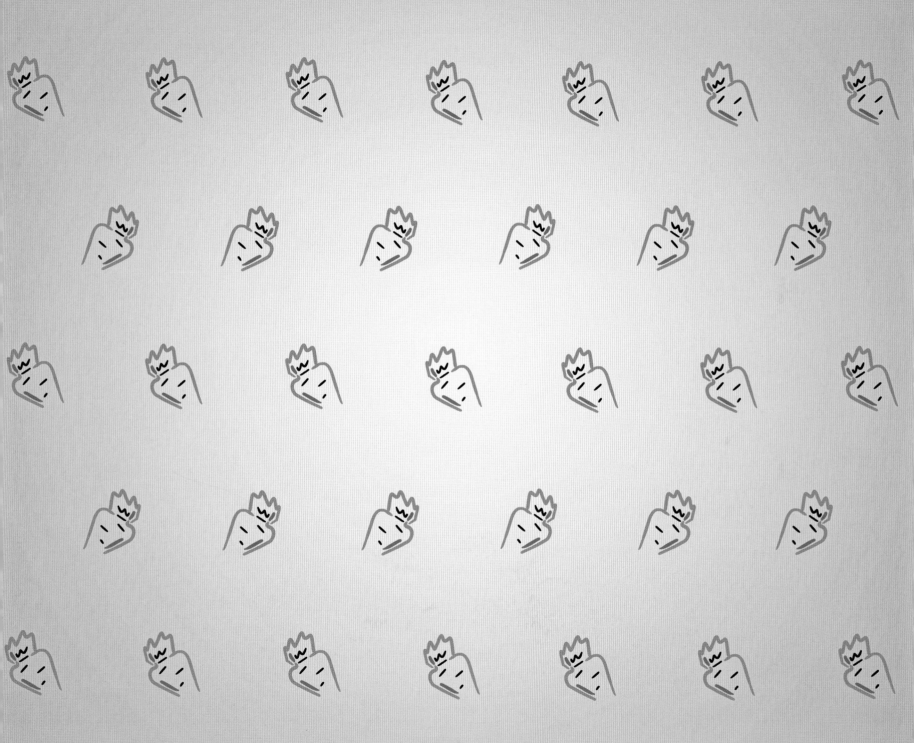

One sleepy eve, in a fruit and veg aisle,
a new delivery makes its arrival.

Fresh produce that's come from all over the globe,
begin to unload into their new home.

Box after box,
     they tumble on through,
          mingling and mixing
               with old friends and new.

WELCOME!

BOING!!

One of them looked to be quite an *odd* fellow,
miSshApen in places with faint hints of yellow.

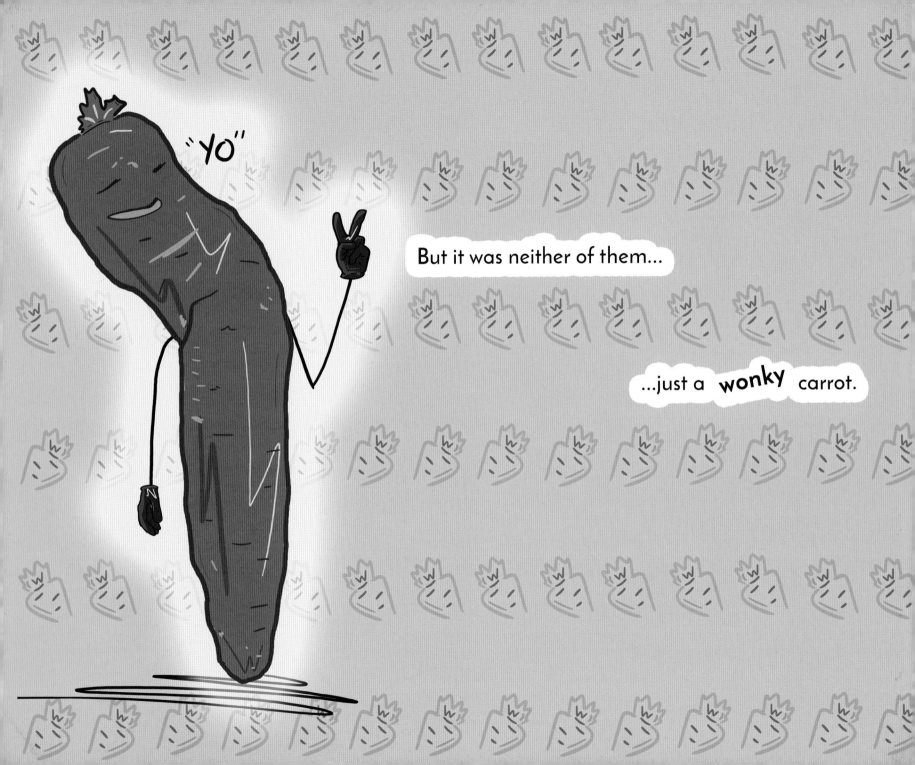

"Good eve!" said Tap, "it's a pleasure to be here!
Don't fret my appearance, there's **nothing** to fear!"

But the fruit and veg were so stunned and confused.
How did something so ***odd*** get out on the loose?

"I'm sorry, wonky carrot,
but you're **not** welcome here,
for not looking perfect
is something we fear."

The carrot just laughed, and
cocked his thumb to his head.

"I'll prove you wrong.
I am perfect!" he said.

That midnight, a ruckus was rearing upstairs.
The fruit and veg shuffled towards it in pairs.

Where were they going? Tap hadn't a clue.
So he asked a radish at the back of the queue.

"Excuse me!" said Tap,
"**where** is it you are going?

And **what** is the cause?
I have no way of knowing!"

"You mean you don't know of the beauty contest?" the radish asked Tap. **"It's the best of the best!"**

"The perfect get picked, it's a close competition... ...scores of 8s and 9s, even 10s can be given."

The carrot looked back with a gleam in his eye.

"Then I will enter and **win**, you cannot deny!"

But instead of supporting the carrot with cheering, the radish gave Tap a smirk and a jeering.

"I'm sorry, wonky carrot, but you're **not** welcome here, for not looking perfect is something we fear."

The carrot just laughed, and cocked his thumb to his head.

"I'll prove you wrong. **I am perfect!**" he said.

The very next day, Tap went on a quest, to find out who led the beauty contest.

He discovered a name from an old broad bean. That name was Beatrice, the Blueberry Queen.

Tin Can Alley

"Great! I will find her and introduce myself, and **prove** there's a place for me here on this shelf!"

As soon as Tap found her, he greeted the queen and her artichoke guards who looked very mean.

The carrot asked if he could enter her show, but the queen's response was nothing short of a no...

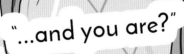

"I'm sorry, wonky carrot, but you're **not** welcome here, for not looking perfect is something we fear."

The carrot just laughed, and cocked his thumb to his head.

"I'll prove you wrong. **I am perfect!**" he said.

The queen was impressed with the carrot's resolve. How could something so *wonky* be ever so bold?!

"Very well wonky carrot I'll grant your request, if you can **prove** your worth with these three trying tests...

...Pass these tests three and you can enter the show, when the people will choose if you should stay or go."

Using blindfolds and noses,
the first test was smell.

"Perfect?" quizzed Beatrice,
"My methods will tell!"

The grapes were summoned to aid the inspection,
blindfolded to test the carrot's perfection.

They circled round Tap and each took a **big** sniff,
then pondered the question,
and had one more whiff.

With their duty complete and their eyes now uncovered,
the grapes told the queen what it was they discovered.

"There's no mistaking the smell we did smells,
he's a **perfect** carrot from what we can tells."

The carrot rejoiced for the answer was true!
The queen, unmoved, brought on test number two.

The next test was taste, with a stray dog named Terry, who was **very** good friends with the royal blueberry.

"My tongue is so special, it can find out the truth. I can taste if you're perfect or just a bad spoof!"

He then approached Tap and gave him one mighty lick. Oh how Terry's drool was so gooey and **thick!**

so lick

After a moment of pause Terry turned to the queen, and gave her his verdict on the weird orange thing.

"He tastes like a carrot, a **perfect** one even.
Perhaps he is right, perhaps we believe him."

The carrot rejoiced for they had started to see!
The queen, unmoved, brought on test number three.

very hi
five

The last test would **challenge** the carrot's condition.
Was he in fact empty or **full** of nutrition?

"Lift up this here pumpkin, let's see if you're **tough!**"

the queen **ordered** Tap,
calling out his bluff.

It's all
in the
veg

EAT WELL
DO WELL
LIVE WELL

Focus
your
mind

Although the pumpkin was 10 times his size,
Tap **did** lift him, and **yelled** up to the skies.

"Here behold my A-1 condition!
I am **not** empty, but **full** of nutrition!"

The queen and her servants were shocked and amazed;
the carrot passed **all** tests and relished her praise.

"Well, wonky carrot, you've **proven** your mettle.
There's just one more thing we need to settle.

You may enter the contest and prove yourself right,
but it's down to the people on your grand night.

They may need some swaying, so win over their hearts.
Explaining what matters is a good way to start."

"Thank you, my Queen, I know **just** what to say!"

And with a smile and a bow, Tap continued his way.

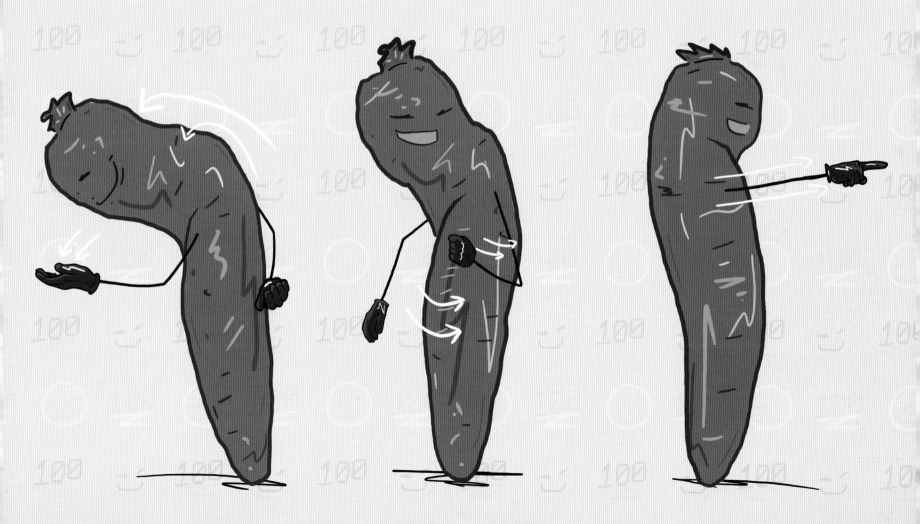

At midnight, the carrot was ready to shine.
He stood in his place, which was fifth in line.

One by one, they walked out through the door,
to a cheering crowd and a very high score.

Some 8s and some 9s, and even some 10s,
Tap kept hearing again and again.

"Get ready carrot, you're the next one out,"

said the veg in charge - a stressed Brussels sprout.

The carrot walked out and awaited his cheers,
but instead he was greeted with silence and fear...

The crowd looked at Tap and began to boo.
The scores - they were **terrible**! A one...a two...a...

"STOP!!"

yelled the carrot. His voice was **strong,**

"Can you **not** see how this is all wrong?"

"It's **not** what we look like that makes us ideal.
It's not a perfect round bulb or a blemish-free peel.

"For we **all** have our wonks, our warts and our spots.
Just remember we all come from the same food plots.

"We're the same from within where our true value lies,
if we just start to see it with more than our eyes.

"So let's **love** our weird shapes and our wonderful form.
Let's make our quirky good looks the accepted norm."

What words to behold! But were they a **hit**?
Tap wasn't quite sure, so he waited a bit.

The crowd sat in the silence brought on from the speech,
when up from the back spoke a lone doughnut peach.

It started with one...
and then a few more...
till the rest of the crowd could say for sure...

The carrot was right! Now who would have guessed
that something ***so wonky*** would win the contest?!

The crowd filled the stage with their cheers again,
to three 9s...no, wait, a **10, 10, 10!**

"You're right, wonky carrot,
you **are** welcome here,
for not looking perfect
is **nothing** to fear!"

The carrot just smiled, with his thumb to the crowd.
He'd won them all over, and boy, he felt **proud!**

"At last," thought Tap, "they can finally see,
there is **nothing wrong** with being wonky!"

So the next time you find yourself quick to dismiss
something or someone by appearance, know this:

Looking perfect means little because in the end,
it's what's on the inside that matters, my friend!

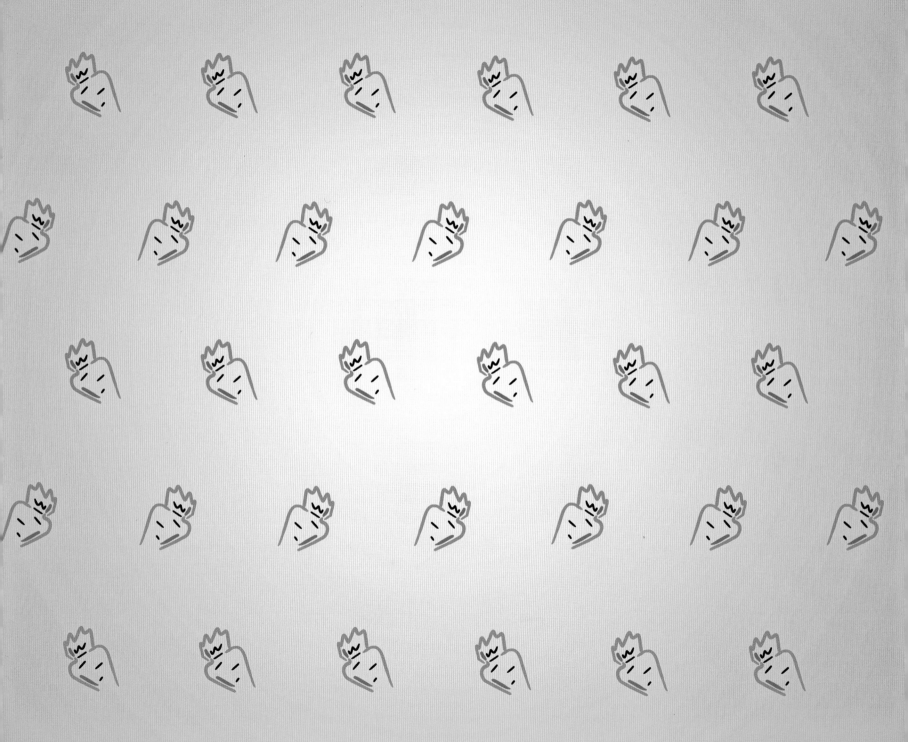

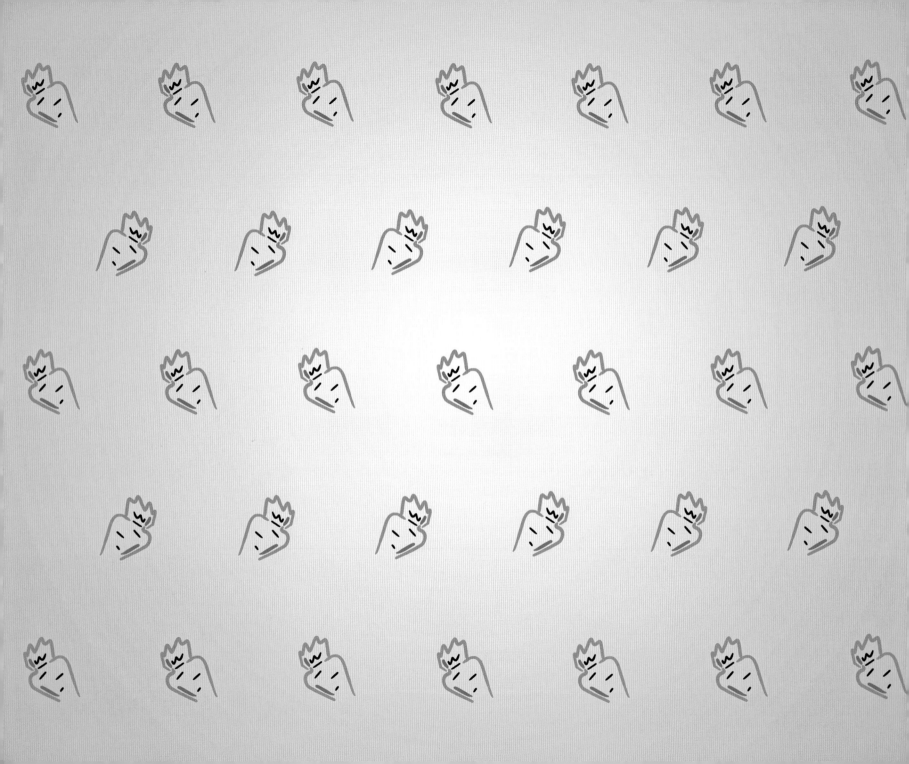

Thanks and final words...

This book was written in response to the amount of perfectly good food that is wasted at retail and consumption level.

Around a third of the food grown globally for us gets wasted every year. That's around 1.3 billion tonnes , or around 102 million double-decker buses*.

Fruits, vegetables, roots and tubers are some of the most affected foods - around 45% grown gets thrown away**.

*,** Source: Food and Agriculture Organization of the United Nations, 2017, FAO and Messe Düsseldorf, SAVE FOOD: Global Initiative on Food Loss and Waste Reduction, http://www.fao.org/save-food/en/d/en/ . Reproduced with permission.

One of the causes of this waste is the way our food looks.

Wonky and blemished fruit and vegetables, just like our friend Tap, may not look perfect, but they still hold all the important nutrients and goodness needed for a healthy diet.

Fruit and vegetables naturally grow in odd shapes due to the environmental conditions they are grown in. The amount and quality of sun, water and soil are some examples that can influence their shape and appearance.

Unfortunately, due to strict rules, supermarkets are less likely to accept these wonderfully wonky and charming fruits and vegetables as the standard. Supermarkets are in favour of consistent height, shape and colour with no blemishes, and anything else gets thrown away and wasted.

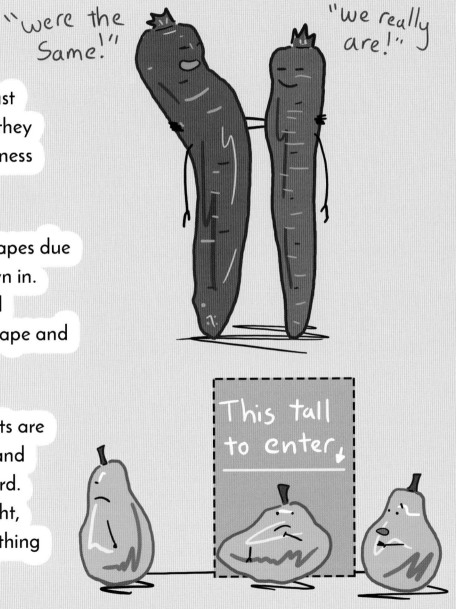

"we're the Same!"

"we really are!"

This tall to enter

The blame can't solely be on the supermarket's standards, however. We as the consumer must remember there is nothing bad about not-so-perfect produce.

To purchase and consume them is totally fine. If we reduce our waste, we'll benefit by saving money, the environment, and resources.

As customers, we all have the choice in what we buy. By understanding how produce is grown, we can encourage retailers to drop their artificial specifications, supplying us fruit and veg regardless of shape and appearance, at a fair price for everyone.

So, next time when you are out food shopping, keep your eyes peeled to see if you've bagged yourself any wonky fruit or veg.

The change is already happening. Supermarkets are beginning to introduce wonky fruit and veg ranges that are both popular and affordable.

By purchasing and consuming them, you will be helping support our farmers, packers, and the fight against food waste. Together we can create the change for a healthier food system.

WE NEED YOUR SUPPORT

TO HELP END FOOD WASTE

Thank you for reading this book. I hope it highlights the
need for change in the way we buy and consume fruit and
veg in a fun and engaging way.

SUPPORTERS

With thanks to everyone for their support during the creation and publication of this book -

Bubble & Squeak

Bubble & Squeak is kids-run social enterprise fighting food waste from the school playground.
They distribute surplus food to their local community, run surplus food events and sell their wonky fruit and veg artwork and chutneys. They are based in East Acton, West London.

www.bubblesqueakeat.com/

Change Food

Change Food is a grassroots movement creating a healthy, equitable food system from the ground up. Through conferences, events and special projects, Change Food provides a platform for voices and ideas that might not otherwise be heard, and works to develop partnerships and collaborations to strengthen the impact of small food producers and organizations toward a truly equitable, sustainable future.

www.changefood.org/

The Felix Project

The Felix Project is a charity that works with food suppliers and charities to reduce food waste and food poverty. We collect food from supermarkets, wholesalers and other food suppliers - food that is fresh and nutritious, but cannot be sold for various reasons. We then deliver that food free of charge to a range of charities across London who provide meals, snacks or food parcels for their clients.

thefelixproject.org/

Foodtank

Food Tank is one of the fastest growing nonprofit organizations around food and agriculture issues, focused on building a global community for safe, healthy, nourished eaters. Their work spotlights environmentally, socially, and economically sustainable ways of alleviating hunger, obesity, and poverty, and create networks of people, organizations, and content to push for food system change.

foodtank.com/

Oddbox

Oddbox is a social enterprise that fights food waste on UK farms. It sources wonky and surplus produce for a fair price from farms, delivers a weekly wonky fruit & veg box which is 30% cheaper than similar services to homes and offices, and donates up to 10% of it's produce to food poverty charities.

www.oddbox.co.uk/

Plan Zheroes

Plan Zheroes are a charity getting great surplus food to people who need it. They are a free food donation platform, where businesses can donate their surplus food to local charities. They also run several volunteer led market collections including London's iconic Borough Market.

planzheroes.org/

ABOUT ME

Christopher Newman, AKA Newmany, is a creative thinker and illustrator from southeast London, UK.

He was born and raised in Thamesmead, before setting off for Cornwall to study BA Creative Advertising at Falmouth University.

With a First-class honours degree under his belt, Newmany decided to use his skills to create helpful and meaningful content to raise awareness of, and tackle global issues that currently affect us and the world we inhabit.

'The Perfectly Wonky Carrot' is Newmany's debut book.

Looking to work together? Have an idea or question?
Drop us a line at info@newmany.co.uk

Question supplied by Foodtank.
"What inspired you to write The Perfectly Wonky Carrot?"

"Halfway through 2016, I watched 'Hugh's War on Waste' - a three-part BBC series that looks into the waste generated by supermarkets and the fast food Industry. The first episode is about the food we eat, and how we - the purchaser, and supermarkets - the supplier; waste millions of tonnes of food each year.

One scene that struck me in particular, featuring some parsnip farmers; truly highlighted the strict cosmetic standards imposed on farmers by supermarkets, who only want perfectly shaped and sized produce. Everything else that's 'wonky' gets rejected, costing farmers vital resources and money. The scene ends with a dump truck pouring out a weeks-worth of rejected turnips - a pile that is around 20 tonnes and over 10 feet high. Seeing the farmer's plight, and the amount of perfectly edible food unnecessarily wasted motivated me to write a book celebrating wonky fruit and veg."

FOLLOW ME

newmany_

newmany_ You can't beat this one!
Deep, earthy flavours, and a vibrant colour, the
beetroot wasn't always the plump, redish-purple

Hey big people! Follow Tap online to continue the story, and to find out more about the food we eat. You'll also find illustrations, stories and a look into the world of Newmany:

 @newmany_

 @itsnewmany

 newmany.co.uk/

JOIN ME

Join Newmany's newsletter today for first dibs into exclusive content, freebies, industry news, and a sneak peek at what's coming soon.

I'll give you my eguide *'Save Food, Save Money'*, and several printable worksheet lessons for free as a token of my appreciation for our new relationship. How lovely!
Visit *newmany.co.uk/free* to get them.

Free for you!

The Perfectly Wonky Carrot
by Newmany

First edition
1 3 5 7 9 10 8 6 4 2

First published in United Kingdom in 2018
by Binocular Books
Christopher Newman trading as
Binocular Books

www.binocularbooks.com
info@binocularbooks.com

A CIP catalogue record for this book
is available at the British Library

ISBN 978-1-9164555-0-4

Enquiries made to -
info@newmany.co.uk

Printed in England